The Wonderful Stories of Jesus from the New Testament

BOOK ONE

The Palm Tree BIBLE

Stories from Scripture
retold by

JANE FLETCHER
RACHEL HALL
UNA McKENNA
KATHY SINGLETON

Illustrated by
ARTHUR BAKER

First published in 1983 as
Good News from Jesus by Palm Tree Press.

This edition published 1989 in
Great Britain by PALM TREE PRESS
Rattlesden
Bury St Edmunds, Suffolk IP30 0SZ

ISBN 0 86208 103 3

Printed in Hong Kong by Colorcraft Limited.

Contents

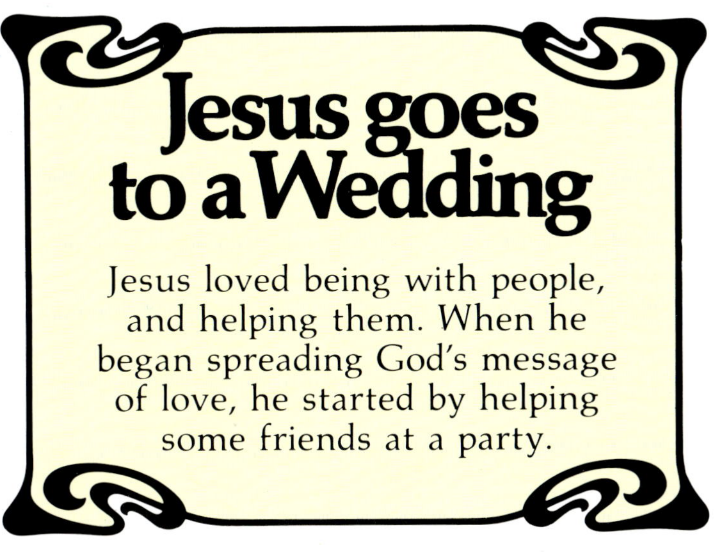

Jesus goes to a Wedding

Jesus loved being with people, and helping them. When he began spreading God's message of love, he started by helping some friends at a party.

One thing Jesus really liked
was being with his friends.

So you can imagine how pleased he was
when he got an invitation
to their wedding
from his friends Rufus and Judith.

"That will be nice,"
he thought to himself.

"I love to hear the wedding prayers,
and there is sure to be
a good time afterwards
for all the guests."

On the day of the wedding
Jesus put on his best clothes,
brushed his hair extra carefully,
and dusted his sandals.

After all,
you didn't go to a wedding every day,
and he wanted everything
to be just right
for Rufus and Judith.

Jesus had arranged
to walk to the wedding
with Mary, his mother,
and some special friends
who had also been invited.

So off they went, down the dusty road,
to join the other guests.

In those days
weddings took place in the evening
when the sun had gone down.

Rufus, the bridegroom,
and all his friends
formed up in a long line.

Then they went to Judith's house
where, together with all her family,
she was waiting.

Rufus and Judith promised
to love each other always,
and to love God especially well.

Everyone prayed for them
and the Rabbi asked God
to bless their marriage.

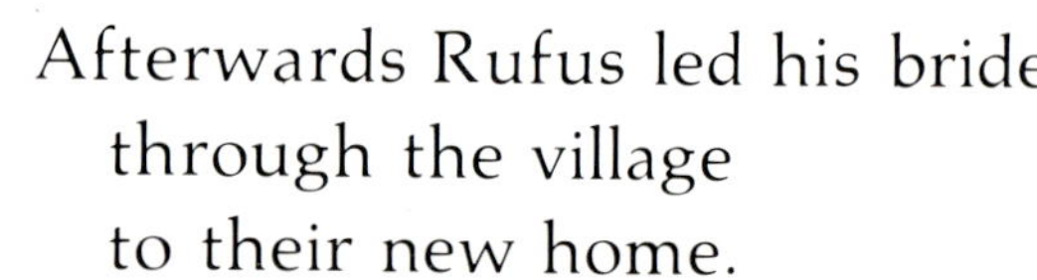

Afterwards Rufus led his bride
through the village
to their new home.

It was dark now,
and all the guests
— with Jesus among them —
lined the way, holding torches.

It was a very pretty sight
and Rufus and Judith
were so obviously in love!

"Doesn't she look lovely,"
the women said to each other
"and just see
how handsome Rufus is today!"

Now the great thing
about a Jewish wedding party
was that it just went on,
and on, and on!

Not for a few hours,
not for a day,
not even for two days.

It could last up to a week!

Poor Rufus,
— although he had made sure
there was plenty of food,
he had slipped up on the wine.

And after a couple of days
it was all gone.

Everyone was very kind about it,
of course.

"Don't worry, Rufus," they said,
slapping him on the back,
"it could have happened to anyone."

When Jesus' mother, Mary, saw
what had happened,
she went over to Jesus.

"They've run out of wine," she said.

Well, Jesus didn't seem
to take much notice
at the time,
but Mary knew he would help.

She took one of the servants aside
and whispered in his ear:
"Now be sure to do
whatever he tells you,
and everything will be all right."

"Right ho!" the servant said.

And sure enough, Jesus did help.

There were six large pots
in one corner of the room.

They were usually full
of water for washing,
but just now they were empty.

"You see those pots,"
Jesus said to the servants,
"I want you to fill them
right up to the top, please."

Well,
the servants moaned
and groaned a bit
— why go
to all that trouble, they said.

But they did as they were asked.

They went in and out,
in and out, in and out,
taking water from the well
and pouring it into the pots.

At last the jars were so full
they were almost overflowing.

"Now I want you
to take a jugful to the man
in charge of the party,"
Jesus said.

"Tell him to taste it."

Well, you should have seen
that man's face
when he tasted it!

He couldn't believe it!

Like all the other people
at the party,
he had watched the servants
filling the jars with water
from the well,
and now . . .
it was no longer water,
it was the tastiest,
juciest, very best . . .
wine!

With that the servants poured out
the new wine.

Everyone had a wonderful time.

There had never been
a wedding like it, they all agreed.

This was Jesus' first miracle
— he had changed
water into wine.

A miracle is a sign
— a sign of the greatness
and glory of God
— a sign that God loves us
and cares for us.

When Mary and the special friends
Jesus took to the wedding
saw what Jesus had done
they believed in him
as the Saviour whom God
had promised to send.

Note for parents:
This story may be found in the Gospel of John, chapter 2, verses 1-12.

Loaves and Fish

After his first miracle Jesus became well known for the way he cared for people. Sometimes they travelled a very long way to hear him speak.

Simon woke up bright and early.
He was so excited.
His cousin, Joel, had come to stay
and they were going fishing.

He yawned and stretched,
then jumped onto Joel's bed.

"Wake up, Jo," he shouted,
"It's a beautiful day."

Jo rubbed the sleep from his eyes
— then he was wide awake, too.

"Come and get your breakfast,"
called Simon's Mum.

They pulled on their clothes,
and gobbled down their breakfast.

"Where's our fishing tackle?"
yelled Simon, hunting around.

"Here you are," said his Mum.
"It's with your lunch basket.
There are some barley loaves
and pickled fish.
Don't forget to be back by sunset,"
she called after them
as they set off down the road.

Just before the Jordan River
Simon shouted to Jo, "This way!"

They turned off the road
and slipped and slithered
down a pathway
to Simon's favourite fishing spot
on the edge of Lake Galilee.

There they fished and played
and sunned themselves.

Jo was skimming stones
across the calm water
when he saw a fishing boat.

"Hey, Simon, look!" he called,
"There's a boat coming in."

They scrambled closer and watched
as the men jumped into the water
and pulled the boat up the sand.

"They don't seem to have caught
any fish," said Simon.

The boys were disappointed.

They decided to go back to their fishing
and playing.

"Let's play hide and seek,"
said Jo after a while.

"Okay, I'll hide," said Simon and ran off
to a secret place near the roadside.

Poor Jo hunted high and low.
He just could not find Simon.

Meanwhile, Simon was watching
the people walking along the road.
There seemed to be hundreds of them
all going in the same direction
in a great hurry.

"The teacher went this way," said one;
"I saw his boat land near here,"
said another.

Then Simon noticed a little girl
hobbling along on a stick.
She sat down on a stone,
and a big tear
trickled down her cheek.

Simon left his hiding place.
"What's wrong?" he asked her.
"I'm looking for Jesus," she sobbed,
"He sailed across the Lake
in a fishing boat with his friends,
but I'm too tired to go any further."

"Never mind," said Simon,

By now, many of the other travellers
had found Jesus and his disciples, too.
So Jesus began talking to the people
and telling them wise stories.

His disciples were moving
among the crowds and bringing the sick
to Jesus to be healed.

The three children watched in wonder:
"He's so kind and gentle and clever,"
they said to each other.

It was getting near suppertime
and the people were hungry.

"I think I know where he is,
and it's not much further."

Just then, Jo appeared:
"Jo, get our things," Simon said.

Then the boys carried the little girl
to the place where they had seen
the men and the fishing boat.

"There he is!" shouted the little girl,
pointing at one of the men
from the boat.

The children heard Jesus
speaking to Philip, a disciple:
"Where can we get food for these people?"

"Lord," said Philip, "we do not have
the money to buy food for them all.
Send them to the farms
and nearby villages and
let them buy their own food."

"But they have all come
a long way and are tired," said Jesus.

Simon noticed the disciple, Andrew,
standing nearby.

"Please, sir," Simon said,
tugging at his sleeve,
"we have five loaves and two fish
you can have."

"That's very kind of you,"
said Andrew, taking Simon to Jesus.

Simon gave the loaves and fish
to Jesus.
"Thank you," said Jesus,
"this is just what we need,"
and he told the crowd to sit down.

Jesus took the bread,
thanking God for providing it,
broke it into pieces,
and handed it round.

Then he did the same with the fish.

"Surely he's not going to feed
all these people
with just our food?" said Jo.

Sure enough, Jesus did just that!

By his power, the bread and fish
were made to go round,
and there was enough for all.

When everyone had eaten,
Jesus told his disciples
to collect up the remains.

There were twelve baskets full!

The children could not
believe their eyes!

Jesus looked at them and smiled.

He had worked a miracle
with their food.

But it was late now, and the
sun was beginning to set.

"Come on," said Simon,
"we'd better be going home."

"Where will you stay?"
Jo asked the little girl.

"Don't worry," said Andrew,
"we'll take care of her."

They knew she was in good hands
as they waved goodbye
to their new friends.

Then they ran all the
way home.

They couldn't wait to tell everyone
about the exciting things
they had seen and heard that day.

"This has been the best day
of my life," shouted Jo.

"Mine too," Simon shouted back
happily.

Note to parents:
This story can be found in the Gospel of John,
chapter 6, verses 1 to 15.

The Good Samaritan

Jesus often spoke to large crowds. He told them stories to show them how much God loved them, and how they should love each other.

Once upon a time,
there was a Jewish trader called Abie.

He lived in Jerusalem
but his work often took him to
far away places.

One day Abie decided to visit
the markets of Jericho.

So, he loaded his donkey
with rich materials.
He packed some clothes and food
and kissed his family good-bye.

It was a long way to Jericho,
and Abie had to walk all the way.

The dusty road led up into the hills,
and wound steeply down
on the other side
towards Jericho.

There were huge rocks on either side
of the twisting, turning road
and guess who had hidden
behind those big boulders . . .?

A band of nasty robbers!

They lay in wait for any travellers
who passed by,
knives at the ready
and eyes glinting greedily.

Abie didn't know what was
in store for him.

He trudged wearily
to the top of the hill.
"Phew, its hot," he muttered
as he mopped his brow.

Suddenly, the robbers pounced!
Abie fought back bravely
but he was outnumbered.

He was knocked to the ground,
his money and clothes were stolen,
and they even took his donkey!

He was left lying in the dust
and the robbers disappeared
into the hills.

Poor Abie groaned.
He couldn't move at all.
He just lay there,
waiting and hoping
that someone would come along.

After a while, he heard footsteps.
A Jewish priest appeared.
"Surely he will help me,"
thought Abie.

"Tut, tut!" muttered the priest,
"what a mess!
I'll pretend I haven't seen."
So the priest walked by
on the other side of the road.

The sun beat down on Abie.
His throat was dry
and still he couldn't move.

But what was that he could hear . . .
clip-clop, clip-clop, clip-clop . . .
It was a donkey
carrying a Samaritan, called Saul.

Abie's heart sank . . .
the Jews and the Samaritans
were enemies.
They just didn't get on at all.

"He won't stop," Abie thought.

But Saul was different . . .

When he saw Abie
Saul felt sorry for him
and got down off
his donkey.

A little later, a Levite hurried by,
panting heavily.

He was due to help the priest
at the Temple.
and he was late.

"Oh dear, oh dear," he mumbled
when he saw Abie.
"I can't stop or I'll be late . . .
oh dearie me."

And off he went,
leaving poor Abie
lying in the dust.

But Saul didn't mind.
He was glad to help.

He walked slowly
next to the donkey,
as they picked their way
down the hillside
and into the town of Jericho.

Saul took Abie to the inn
where he was staying
and put him to bed.

He reached for his water bottle
and, gently lifting Abie's head,
gave him some water to drink.

"Thank you," gasped Abie weakly.

Then Saul bathed Abie's wounds
and tore up his own coat
to make bandages
for the wounded man.

He lifted him gently
on to the back of his donkey.

Poor Abie was too weak
to stay sitting on the donkey
and he leant heavily on Saul.

All through the night
he looked after Abie,
wiping his brow,
dressing his wounds,
and helping him to sip
a little water.

And, slowly, very slowly,
Abie began to get stronger.

The next morning
Saul had to leave Jericho
but Abie was not well enough
to return to Jerusalem.

So Saul said to the Inn Keeper:
"Abie has no money
but I'll pay for him
until he is better.
Take good care of him."
He gave the man two silver coins.

Then he mounted his donkey,
waved good-bye to Abie,
and set off out to Jericho.

"So you see," Jesus said to the crowd
who were listening to him,
"this story shows that
we should be kind to everyone,
no matter who they are,
whether we know them or not,
or whether we like them or not."

Note for parents:
This story can be found in the Gospel of Luke,
chapter 10, verses 29-37.

The Lost Sheep

Some people don't always love God as they should — they just wander off like a sheep. But you can be sure God will go out and find them again.

This is a story that Jesus told
to a lot of people
who had come to see him.

There was once a shepherd called Ezra,
and his pride and joy were his sheep
— one hundred of them,
all sizes, all shapes, and all colours;
some fat, some skinny,
some very clever,
others just a little slow to catch on.

But, whether they were big or small,
black or white, brainy or slow
didn't matter one little bit to Ezra.

He loved them all the same.

And because he loved them all,
he gave each one a name.

There were Betty and Barney,
Minnie and Mike, Alice and Archie,
Wooly and Walter,
Mandy and Montgomery,
Rosie and Roger . . .
and so many more
that it would take the rest
of this book
to give all their names!

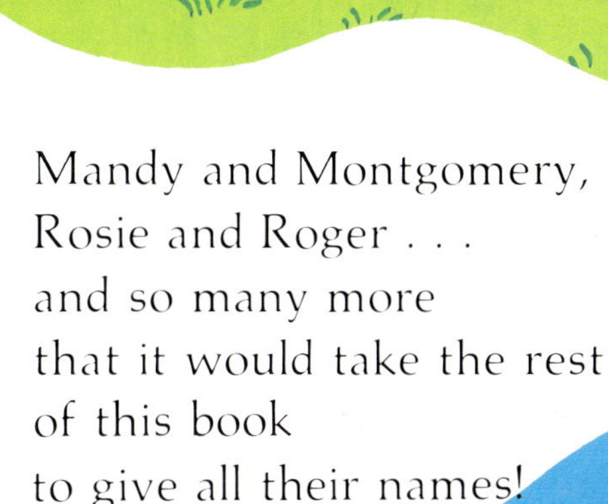

They were happy sheep
who spent their time
chewing away in Ezra's field.

The river that ran by
at the bottom of the field
watered the land
so that the grass was always
thick and juicy.

Ezra's sheep were very lucky!

But one day a dreadful thing happened.

Ezra woke early,
looked out of his tent at the sheep
and knew right away
that something was wrong.

Without even counting his sheep,
he knew that one was missing.

And very quickly
he realised that it was Henry,
a friendly, fluffy little sheep
who was not there.

Without even stopping to think,
Ezra grabbed his walking stick
and set off to look for Henry.

For the moment
Henry was all that mattered to him.

The other sheep
— the ninety-nine left in the field —
could take care of themselves
for now.

Ezra walked for miles
calling Henry's name
— up hills, down dales, across streams,
over fields, never stopping to rest,
only thinking all the time of Henry.

The day grew hotter,
and there was little shade.

Ezra felt really glummy, but still
he searched, and searched,
and searched.

Until . . .

. . . at last, a long, long way away,
he saw . . .
Henry, the lost sheep.

Zoom!
You could almost hear Ezra make that
noise as he rushed to be with Henry.
Zoom!

When Ezra reached Henry,
he caught hold of his lost sheep
and gave him a big hug.

"Henry, I'm so pleased to see you!"
he said. "I'd almost given up hope
of seeing you again."

With that,
Ezra lifted Henry
onto his shoulders
and they set off for home.

Ezra was so pleased at finding Henry
that he waved to everyone they met
and shouted:
"I had lost one of my sheep,
but now I have found him."

And, of course,
everyone was very pleased for Ezra.

"I had lost a sheep
and now I have found him!"
he told them all.
"Come to my party to celebrate!"

And what a party it was!
They danced and sang
far into the night.

Everyone was so pleased
at Ezra's good news.

"Just imagine,"
they said to each other,
"Ezra has found his lost sheep."

Well, all those people
sitting listening to Jesus
thought that was a very
good story.

When they came to Ezra's field,
all the other sheep were waiting
to say hello to Henry.

They licked him all over,
and gave him a good meal
of juicy grass.

You could hear their happy "baa's"
all over the village!

As for Ezra,
he sent out invitations
to all his friends and neighbours.

We must always try to be good,
but no matter
how naughty we are,
our Father in heaven
will always forgive us
if we ask him.

Like Ezra,
he will do everything he can
to find us if we
go away from him,
and when he does find us
he will be very happy.

Note for parents:
This story can be found in the Gospel of Luke,
chapter 15, verses 3-7,
and in the Gospel of Matthew,
chapter 18, verses 12-14

And they liked it even more
when Jesus went on to explain
that we are all like sheep,
and that our Father in heaven
is our Shepherd.

And just as Ezra loved all his sheep,
our Father in heaven
loves each one of us
very, very much.

He loves us so much
that he does not want to lose
even one of us.

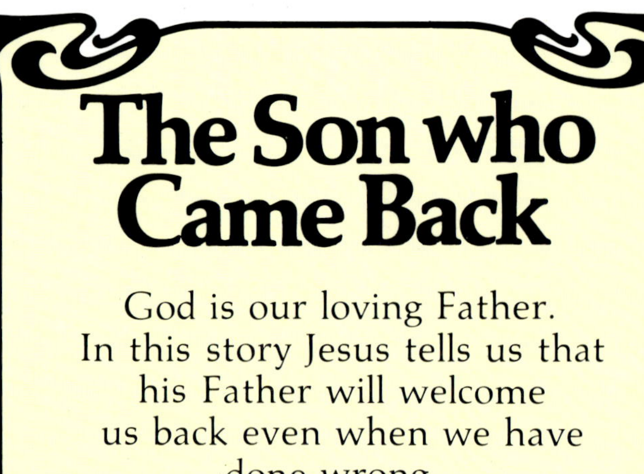

The Son who Came Back

God is our loving Father.
In this story Jesus tells us that
his Father will welcome
us back even when we have
done wrong.

Once upon a time,
there was a family —
a mother and father and two sons.

They had a big house and lots of
servants to look after them.

One day,
the younger son,
who was called
Sam,
said to his father:

"Dad, when you die
half of all your lands and
riches will be mine.
But I don't want to wait that long.
Can I have it all now?"

To Sam's surprise his father agreed,
and gave him half of everything
he had.

Sam took it all,
loaded it up on to a big cart,
and set off for the city.

"With all this money to spend
I'll have a really great time,"
he thought to himself.

Sam was so silly— he thought that
money would bring happiness.

When he reached the city, he
found a beautiful house to live in,
bought expensive furniture,
hired lots of servants
and lived a lazy life of luxury.

And, of course,
everybody came to his parties,
everybody waved to him in
the street,
everybody wanted him as their friend.

Until . . .

One day Sam found he had spent
all his money, and suddenly
he couldn't afford his house any more,
all the furniture had to be sold,
and the servants left because he
couldn't pay their wages.

And, worst of all,
the people he had thought
were his friends
didn't want to be his friends any more.

Some days later
his father was just finishing his dinner
when he looked out of the window and saw Sam coming in the distance.

He jumped out of his seat,
rushed straight out of the house,
and . . .

He took Sam in his arms and kissed him.
"Dad," said Sam, with tears rolling down his cheeks,

Sam was all alone.
He had no money for food. He had no friends, and he missed his family

The only job he could find was feeding pigs.

One day, as he was shuffling round
giving the pigs their breakfast,
he thought to himself:

"I'm here starving, while at home
my father's servants have plenty to eat."

"I'll go home and tell my father I'm sorry
for all the wrong things I have done.
Then he might take me on
as one of his servants."

So, Sam, hungry, tired, and
very unhappy,
set off on the long journey home.

"I have disobeyed God and
made you very unhappy.
I'm sorry. Please forgive me."

His father was so happy
that Sam had come back,
and he forgave him readily.

He said to his servants:
"Bring out the best clothes for my son.
Put a beautiful ring on his finger.
Find some comfortable shoes,
and prepare a wonderful feast.
We'll celebrate my son's return!"

While all this was going on,
Sam s elder brother, Matthew,
was coming home from the fields
where he had been working.

When he heard the music and dancing
he called over one of the servants,
and asked him: "What's all that noise?"

"Your brother has returned,"
the servant said,
"and your father is having a party
for him."

Matthew was cross.
Even his father could not
get him to join the party.

"All these years I've been
a good son to you,"
Matthew said to his father,
"but you have never given a party
for me."

"But when Sam comes home
after spending all that money,
you treat him like a king."

"Matthew," his father replied,
"you are always with me,
and everything I have is yours."

"Sam had left us and behaved badly,
but now he has come back.
Our family is together again."

And with that
they both went in
to join the rest of their family
and friends at the party.

Everyone was happy because
the lost son had come home.

Note for parents:
This story may be found in the Gospel of Luke, chapter 15, verses 11-32.

Evil Beezil's Wicked Trick

The Good News Jesus bought was meant for everyone. But in this story Jesus warned people what would happen if they refused to listen to him.

Jesus had been working very hard,
and he needed a good rest.

So, one morning,
when he woke up to a beautiful day,
he thought to himself:
"I'll have a few hours off
and take it easy down by the lake."

He collected some of his friends
and off they went with some food
and a towel in case the water
was warm enough for a swim.

But no sooner
had they reached the lake
when word got around
that Jesus was there.

"That wonderful preacher, Jesus,
is down by the lake . . .",
people said to each other,
". . . you know, the one
who teaches us wonderful things,
who heals the sick
and tells us to love each other."

It was not long before
they all made their way to the lake.

And it was not long before
Jesus realised
he was not going to get any rest!

The people really wanted
Jesus to speak to them,
but the ground where they were
all standing was rather flat,
and they could not see him very well.

So Jesus got into a boat
that was tied up nearby.

making sure that every inch of the soil
was covered with seed.

"Well done, everyone!" said Jethro
when they had finished.
"You've earned yourselves a slap up meal
and a good night's rest."

The trouble was they slept too well . . .

That was better – when he stood up
they could all see him,
and Jesus had a good strong voice,
so they could hear him as well!

He told them stories
that showed them how they should live,
and this is one of the stories he told:

A man called Jethro had a lovely big field.

"This year," Jethro thought to himself,
"I shall sow some really good seed
in that field of mine.
Then I shall have a fine crop of wheat
in the summer."

So, with the help of Asher and Gad,
who worked for him,
Jethro set about sowing.

First, they dug up the field
so that the earth was fresh
and free of weeds.

Then they worked from morning to night

. . . because nobody
saw Evil Beezel
creep into the field
in the dark of the night.

As usual Evil Beezel was up to no good.

He hated to see a nice, well-sown field
with good healthy wheat in it.

So do you know what he did?
He sowed nasty, prickly weeds
among the wheat.

"Ha, ha!" he chuckled to himself
as he did his wicked work,
"my weeds will kill all this nice wheat.
That will give everyone
a very nasty shock!"

Evil Beezel was happy only
when he was
making someone else unhappy.

For a time
nobody knew what had happened.

Each day Jethro and Asher and Gad
went to see
how the seeds were coming along.

Gradually the seeds began to grow
into lovely big shoots of wheat.

The earth in Jethro's field was rich,
and there was just the right amount
of rain and sun that year
for a really good crop.

Jethro was a happy man.

Until one day the weeds
that Evil Beezel had sown
began to pop up all over the place.

At first they were just little weeds,
but soon they grew into big,
bullying weeds and made the wheat
very unhappy.

"We'll be choked to death!"
the wheat said to each other.
"Help!"

As soon as Asher and Gad
saw the big, bullying weeds,
they ran to tell Jethro.

"We worked so hard to make sure
there were no weeds
in that field before sowing,"
they said sadly.
"What has happened?"

Jethro thought for a moment
and then said:
"The only thing I can think of
is that we have an enemy.
Someone has planted
those weeds in my field.
Someone is trying
to kill my wheat."

"Well, we've got to do something about it!"
Asher said. "Shall we pull up the weeds?"

"No, no!" Jethro replied. "That way
you might pull up the wheat too,
and then we would have lost everything.
It's better to take a chance
and let the wheat and the weeds
grow side by side
until we are ready to gather in the crop."

"Then," Jethro continued
while Asher and Gad listened carefully,
wondering what he had in mind,
"I will tell
the men who gather in the harvest
to sort out the wheat from the weeds.

"We'll store the wheat carefully in my barn.
It will be safe and dry in there.

"As for the weeds, we shall tie those
in bundles and throw them onto the fire."

By this time it was getting dark
and Jesus had finished telling his stories,
so the crowd started drifting away.

They didn't really want to go
because they loved being with Jesus,

but there was dinner to cook
and the children to get to bed.

As usual, Jesus and his friends
enjoyed their dinner that evening.
They liked being together
and they usually talked about the things
they had done that day.

"I liked your stories, Jesus," one of them said,
"but what did you mean by that one
about the weeds and the wheat?
Will you tell us?"

"Of course I will," Jesus replied.
"You just have to imagine that I am
the man who planted the seeds of wheat.

"The wheat that sprung up
is all the good people who follow my ways.

"But Evil Beezel is the Devil,
and his weeds are all the wicked people
who will not listen to me."

"And you remember that when
the harvest was gathered in
the wheat was separated from
the weeds?
In just the same way,
the good people will be separated
from the bad people by God's angels.

"The good people will live
with my Father in heaven for ever
and ever.

"The bad people will never see
my Father, and they will be
punished for doing wrong."

Jesus's friends
were very impressed by that story,
and they all went to sleep
determined to do as Jesus says.

Note for parents:
This story may be found in the Gospel of Matthew,
chapter 13, verses 24-30 and 36-43.

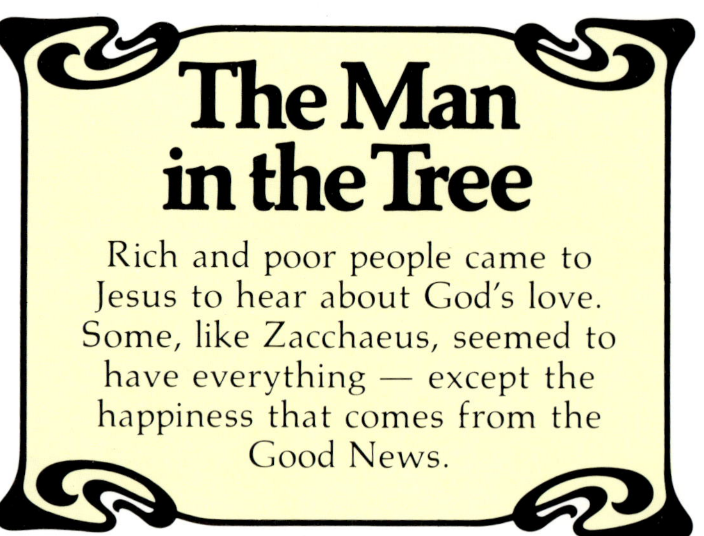

The Man in the Tree

Rich and poor people came to Jesus to hear about God's love. Some, like Zacchaeus, seemed to have everything — except the happiness that comes from the Good News.

Zacchaeus lived in a very fine house
on the edge of a town called Jericho.

His house was big and richly furnished.

He had lots of servants and plenty of food.

In fact,
he had everything he could wish for,
except one thing . . .

He had no friends!
No-one ever came to visit him.
No-one ever came to eat with him.

Poor Zacchaeus —
he was very rich,
but he was also very lonely.

Each evening, as the sun was setting,
he'd look out down the road
that led to the city,
hoping that someone might come.

And each evening . . . no-one came.

You see . . .
Zacchaeus was a tax collector:
he collected money
from all the people in the town
for the Roman governor to use.

Even the very poor people
were forced to pay their taxes
and their families go hungry.

So, the townsfolk hated Zacchaeus,
and to make matters worse
Zacchaeus used to overcharge them
and keep the extra money
for himself!

Zacchaeus was a small man
and could not see over
the shoulders of the people,
even when he stood on tip-toe!

He could not push through
to the front either —
the people knew who he was
and pushed and knocked him
or just sneered and blocked his way.

What was he to do?

He looked around and there . . .
a little way ahead,
at the edge of the crowd,
was a strong, sturdy sycamore tree.

One day, while collecting taxes
at his table in the market place,
he overheard some women talking:

"They say Jesus, the miracle-worker,
is heading this way."

"Yes, he should come down
the main street."

"I've heard he teaches wisely
and knows a lot,
yet he mixes with all sorts
of people, good and bad."

Zacchaeus was curious.
He wondered what this
man, Jesus, was like,
and decided to go and see him.

A big crowd had begun
to line the main street.

If he could climb up into its branches,
he would be able to see Jesus
over the heads of the people . . .
that would show them!

So, off he ran, down the road
to the sycamore tree.

The bottom branches were quite high
and he had to jump to catch hold of one.

Then, with a heave he swung his legs up
and pulled himself up
till he was sitting on the lowest branch.

"Oooh, I hope I don't fall,"
he thought to himself as he climbed higher.

Soon, Jesus and his disciples
appeared in the distance
followed by the large crowd,
all wanting his attention

But, in the middle of all the noise,
Jesus looked up
and saw Zacchaeus sitting in the tree,
and said to him: "Hurry down, Zacchaeus,
I'm coming to your house
for a meal tonight."

Zacchaeus couldn't believe his ears!
How did Jesus know his name?
And if he knew his name,
then he must know that
Zacchaeus was a tax collector,
and no-one spoke to tax collectors,
let alone had supper with them.

He scratched his head in puzzlement,
and slowly, a big grin
spread across his face.

Jesus did know his name
and what he was
and Jesus still wanted to be with him!

It didn't matter to Jesus
how bad he had been!

Zacchaeus jumped out of the tree
and pushed his way through the crowd
towards Jesus.

"You're very welcome to come to my house
and eat with me tonight," he said to Jesus.
"I shall go and make the arrangements
right away."

Zacchaeus ran on ahead: he was so excited —
at last, someone was coming to visit him
at his home.

The people in the crowd grumbled
to each other:
"Jesus shouldn't eat with the likes
of Zacchaeus. He's a cheat and a liar"

"Jesus is too good for him."

"He shouldn't mix with wicked men
like Zacchaeus."

Jesus heard what they were saying
and it made his heart sad
that they should hate
people like Zacchaeus so much.

Jesus and his disciples
walked up the lonely road
to Zacchaeus' big house.

Zacchaeus welcomed them warmly
and they sat down to supper.

They spent many hours
eating and talking.

Zacchaeus felt so happy
that this very special man
had taken the time
and the trouble
to come and be with him.

As he and his disciples got ready
to leave,
he said to Zacchaeus:
"Today you have left your
old and wicked ways behind you
and begun a new life.
That is why I have come."

Then they left Zacchaeus
smiling happily in his new life,
and continued on their journey.

And Zacchaeus knew he would
never be lonely again.

Note for parents:
This story can be found in the Gospel of Luke, chapter 19, verses 1 to 10.

He realised Jesus cared about him,
and how wrongly he had been living.

In fact, Jesus' visit
had meant so much to Zacchaeus
that he decided to live
a new life from that moment on.

He stood up and said to Jesus:
"I have lied to many people,
and cheated them,
but I want to live an honest life
from now on.
I shall give half of everything
I own to the poor people,
and whoever I have cheated,
I will pay back four times
as much!"

Jesus was pleased.

Lionel, the Lame Man

The power of Jesus' love made sick people well again. It also helped them to be sorry if they had done bad things.

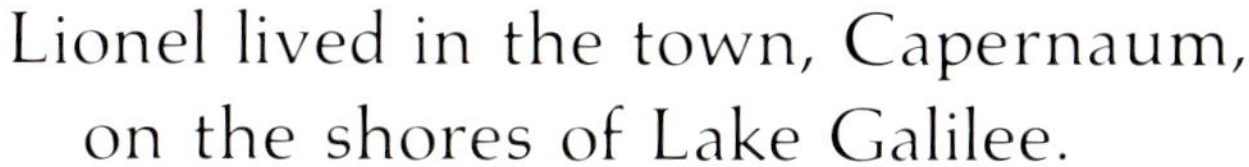

Lionel lived in the town, Capernaum,
on the shores of Lake Galilee.

Lionel was a lame man
which meant he couldn't walk and run
like his friends.

He just had to sit on his mat,
on the sandy ground, all day, every day.

Some days he felt very sorry for himself
and jealous of his friends,
and became very grumpy.

Lionel would shout at them
when they tried to help him.

But his friends knew that he didn't mean it,
and they visited him every day.

They told him the wonderful stories
they had heard about Jesus —
how he made people well again
and how much he loves everyone.

Lionel wished he could meet this man, Jesus.
Maybe, he could make him walk again.

One day . . .
there was great excitement
in the town of Capernaum.

Lionel was lying on his mat
in the hot sun
when he noticed that everyone
was hurrying down to the Lake.

He wondered why.

"Hey, what's going on?" he called,
but nobody heard him.

He tried again, louder:
"Hoi, what's happening?"

This time someone shouted back:
"It's Jesus, the teacher —
his boat has just sailed in!"

Poor Lionel . . .
he did want to see Jesus so very much.

But nobody stopped to take him.
They all just walked on by,
kicking the dust up in the sandy streets,
and left him behind.

Lionel felt angry . . . and sad . . .
all at the same time,
and began to get grumpy again.

Meanwhile, Jesus and his followers
had waded ashore
and were walking to
a friend's house.

They were followed by a large crowd
wanting to hear Jesus speak
and see him heal the sick.

There were old people, young people;
men, women and children;
blind people who could not see;
deaf people who could not hear;
mothers with sick babies;
people on crutches, limping;

and some people even brought
their animals to be healed!

But Lionel was not forgotten . . .

His four friends had seen the crowd
and knew Jesus had come.
They left work early and went to
fetch Lionel.

He was sulking, grumpily, on his mat.
"Where have you been?"
grumbled Lionel.
"Jesus will never see me now —
there are too many people," he moaned.

"Don't worry," said Ben,
"we'll think of something."

The four friends each took
a corner of Lionel's mat
and carried him down the road.

When they got to the house,
the crowd was even bigger.
They were all pushing,
trying to get into the house.

"Oh dear," said Tim,
"we'll never get through that crowd."

"Mmmm," mumbled Bartie,
stroking his chin . . .
"I've got it!" he shouted suddenly.
"Simon, go and fetch some rope
and meet us round the back
of the house. Hurry!"

Simon dashed off and the others
took Lionel to the back of the house.

What do you think
they were going to do? . . .

There was a flight of stairs
leading up to the flat roof.

They carefully carried Lionel
up the stairs and onto the roof!

Then the friends began to scrape away
at the baked clay roof
with sticks and their bare hands.

Soon, a hole appeared
and got bigger . . . and bigger,
until it was big enough for their plan
and they could see Jesus
and the people below them.

Simon came back with the rope
and then they were ready.

Have you guessed what
they were going to do?

They lowered Lionel down
through the hole, still on his mat!
His friends puffed and panted
and strained at the ropes
as Lionel went lower and lower . . .
till he lay at Jesus' feet.

The crowd gasped with surprise.
They couldn't believe their eyes!

Lionel wasn't sure
whether Jesus would be cross or not.

"Please, Jesus," he said, in a shaky voice,
"make me better again."

Jesus smiled at him.
He knew all the trouble his friends
had gone to, to get Lionel to him,
He knew how grumpy Lionel had been too.

"Lionel," he said, "I know you have not
always been good, and grumble a lot."

There was a whisper amongst the crowd.
They nodded their heads —
they all knew Lionel and he felt sorry.

"But," said Jesus, "I forgive you
for all those wrong things."

Lionel looked up at Jesus.
Suddenly, he felt good all over.
He still couldn't move,
but he didn't feel like grumbling!
He felt happy inside.

There were some men in the crowd
who thought only God
could forgive wrong.

(They didn't know that Jesus
is God's Son.)

Jesus knew what they were thinking
and spoke to them.

Then he turned
to Lionel

and said: "Lionel, get up
and take your mat and go home!"

Some men sniggered —
everyone knew Lionel
couldn't move.

They watched . . . and waited . . .
and . . .

Slowly, Lionel . . .
bent and stretched his arms,
then his legs, then he sat up
and then, he stood up!

The people were amazed!

Lionel bent down
and rolled up his mat.

He looked up at his friends
and laughed. He was so happy!

Then he said to Jesus,
"Thank you, Jesus,
for making me better,"
and made his way to the door.

Outside, his friends
were waiting to meet him.

They laughed and joked
and hugged each other —
they were all so happy —
and Lionel thanked them.

"We knew Jesus could
make you better,"
they told Lionel.

As they hopped and skipped
down the dusty street,
they all thanked God
who gave Jesus the power
to make Lionel better again.

Note for parents:
This story can be found in the Gospel of Mark, chapter 2, verses 1-12.

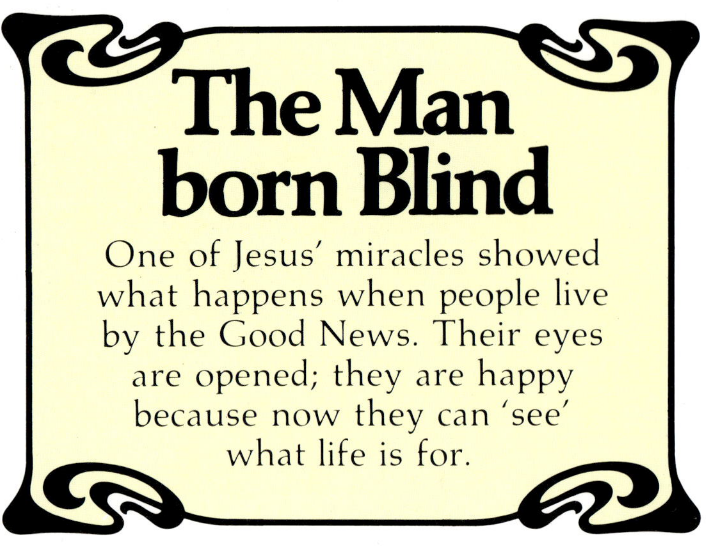

The Man born Blind

One of Jesus' miracles showed what happens when people live by the Good News. Their eyes are opened; they are happy because now they can 'see' what life is for.

Jerusalem was a big city,
and lots of people lived there.

In one part of the city there was a market.

Ephraim, the fishmonger,
sold his fish from a stall.

David, the date-seller, had a smart barrow.

Mordecai, the butcher,
had a real shop on the corner.

And Eli just found the best place
to pile his melons up high.

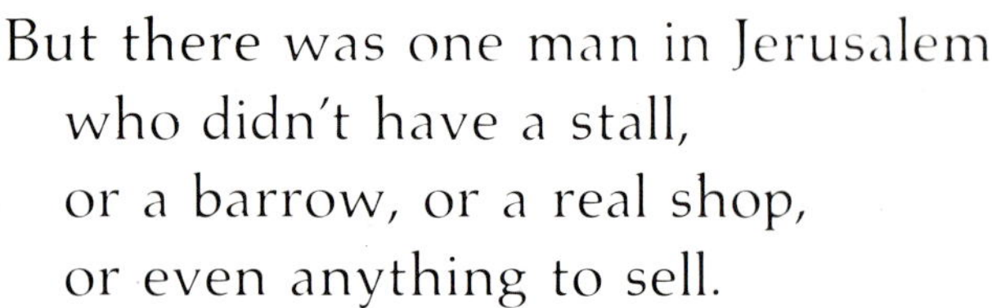

But there was one man in Jerusalem
who didn't have a stall,
or a barrow, or a real shop,
or even anything to sell.

His name was Abner, and he was blind.

Abner's friends had to help him along
so that he wouldn't bump into
other people, or their mules,
or their stalls and barrows,
or squash their fruit and vegetables.

One day Jesus and his friends
were out for a walk in Jerusalem.

There was no market that day
because it was the Sabbath
— the day when everyone rested
and made a special effort
to pray to God.

When they saw Abner
Jesus' friends asked
each other:
"Why has God punished
this man
by making him blind?"

Jesus overheard them.
"You musn't think,
because someone is blind
or sick in any way,
that God is punishing them,"
he said quite firmly. "Not at all!
In fact, God has a very
special love for Abner."

With that, Jesus bent down.

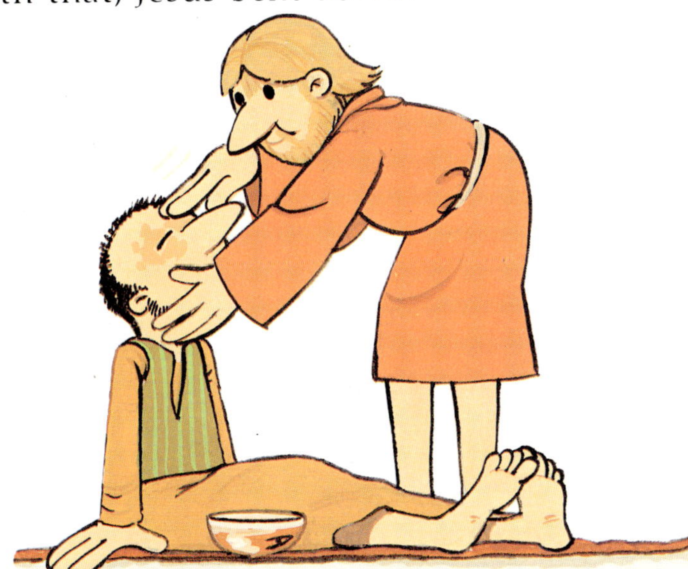

He licked his fingers,
rubbed them in the red, sandy dust,
and mixed a little ball of mud, like paste.

Then, as if it were an ointment,
Jesus spread this mud on Abner's eyes.

The mud made Abner's face quite dirty,
so no one was surprised when Jesus said to him:
"Go and wash at the Pool of Siloam!"

The Pool wasn't far, and Abner
stumbled off, helped by his friends.

He got down beside the Pool
and splashed his face
with the cool, clear water.

Then . . .
when Abner lifted up his head again,
he could see!

Abner was so happy and excited
that he began jumping, and skipping,
telling everyone at the top of his voice:
"I can see! I can see!"

"The man Jesus made a paste,
smoothed it on my eyes,
and told me to wash
at the Pool of Siloam,"
Abner explained,
"so I did what he said,
and now I can see!"

By this time
lots of people were beginning
to crowd around Abner
and they made quite a noise.

The Pharisees
— whose job it was to help
the people keep the Sabbath
day properly,
though they sometimes
overdid it a bit —
were rather anxious
about all the fuss.

It was hard to believe
that this was the same man
— the new Abner was so full of life
and happiness.

The friends
who used to guide Abner along
when he was blind
were quite out of breath
trying to keep up with him!

Abner went dashing back
to where he used to beg.

Ephraim, the fishmonger,
saw him coming and
tried to get his little family
out of the way
in case Abner bumped into them.

But Abner only laughed.
"Don't worry!" he shouted happily,
"I can see as well as you can!"

Ephraim was amazed!
"What happened?" he asked.

So they came along
to see what was going on.

"What's going on here?" they asked,
and once again Abner told them
what had happened.

Some of the Pharisees were angry
when they heard Abner's story.
"Jesus can't go around
doing things like that
on the Sabbath!" they said.

But some other Pharisees
thought it might be all right.
"After all," they said,
"Jesus must be God's friend
to be able to do
such wonderful things."

For a time they argued among themselves,
but they couldn't make up their minds,
so they turned on Abner:
"You're the one who was blind,
what do you think?"

Quick as a flash, Abner said,
"I think Jesus is a prophet, sent by God."

Poor Abner was in trouble all round!
Not only were the Pharisees
making life difficult for him,
but a lot of other people
just didn't believe his story.
They thought he was pretending!

So they decided they would check up
with Abner's parents.
"Is that really your son?"
they asked the old people.

"Of course it is!" Abner's mother replied,
"and you know very well
he's been blind since he was born
— until today, that is."

And Abner's father chipped in:
"But we don't know
any more about it than you do.
Why don't you ask Abner?"

So back they all went
to find Abner once more.

"Now look here,"
they said to him, yet again,
"are you quite sure it was Jesus
who opened your eyes?"

"Well, remember,
I couldn't see at the time," said Abner,
trying to make a joke of it,
"but yes, he spread the muddy paste,
told me to wash, and now I can see."

All this was getting Abner down,
and he was rather angry
that no one would believe him.

"Three times I have
explained to you,
and still you don't believe
that Jesus opened my eyes.
Do you really think that God
would let Jesus do a thing like that
if he was not his friend?"

"What do you know about it?"
the Pharisees shouted at Abner.
"You couldn't even see anything
until today.
Do you know better than us?
We have been reading and
learning from books for years."

And they chased poor Abner away
so that he wouldn't tell
anyone else about Jesus.

Abner was sitting all alone
in the shade of the city wall
when Jesus found him.

"Do you really believe
what you were saying to those people
— that the man who cured you
was sent by God?"
Jesus asked him gently.

"Oh yes, I do, I really do!" said Abner.
"I just wish I knew where to find him."

"Well," said Jesus,
"you're looking at him. It was me."

Abner could hardly
believe his ears.
He fell to his knees
and thanked Jesus.

From that moment on
Abner knew that
Jesus would
always be his
friend,
always there to
help him.

Abner had been blind,
but Jesus had opened his eyes.
Now Abner could see.

Above all, Abner could see Jesus,
he could see that Jesus was sent
by God, that he must love Jesus,
listen to him, and
do what he asked
for the rest of
his life.

Note for parents:
This story is to be found in
the Gospel of John,
chapter 9, verses 1-41.

Barty says Thank You

All the stories and miracles show Jesus' love. People showed their love for Jesus by saying 'thank you'. But not everyone remembered.

Jesus and his friends would often
travel for days at a time.

They loved the countryside,
and when Jesus was not teaching,
or healing people,
or simply dropping a kind word
here and there,
they would all sit down,
have something to eat and drink,
and then rest.

They were a happy group of friends.

Often they would come across
a little village
where the people worked
from morning to night,
looking after the cows
and camels,
the crops
and, of course,
their homes.

One day
when Jesus and his friends
came to one of these villages,
there was a sad sight.

Ten lepers were standing there.
(A leper is a person who has
a nasty skin disease which in
Jesus' time could not be cured.)

They cried out:
"Jesus! Master! Take pity on us!"

They were unhappy men
because all the other people
in the village
would have nothing to do with them.

But Jesus was only too pleased
to see them.
He talked to them for a while,
asking each one his name.

They were:
Izzy, Zadok, Abe, Jo,
Barty, Jude, David, Josh,
Toby and Sam.

The lepers
had many a sad story to tell
about the way
people had treated them
— just because they were
not well!

Then Jesus prayed over them
— he prayed
that their dreadful illness
would be made better.

Now in those days
the only people who could say
if you were better or not
were the priests,
or rabbis, as they were called.

So Jesus said to the ten lepers:
"Go and see the priests
and ask them if you are better."

Well, the lepers couldn't quite
understand why Jesus had said this,
although they hoped that
something wonderful might happen
so off they went,
— limping,
— stumbling,
— some leaning to the right,
— others leaning to the left!

And as they limped
and stumbled along,
they were healed
because Jesus had prayed
that they would be.

And by the time
they had taken off their bandages
to show the priests,
all the lepers
had lovely soft skin again.

They were amazed!
The priests were amazed!
Everyone was amazed!

Of course,
the lepers were very excited,
and they started to plan
a party to celebrate.

This was going to be the party
to end all parties,
they decided!

But they had forgotten something,
hadn't they . . .

They had forgotten to thank Jesus
for making them better.

All except Barty.

He remembered,
and he ran back to Jesus,
shouting at the top of his voice.
"Praise God!"
"Hallelujah!"
"I love you, Lord!"
"God is great!"

He was so grateful to Jesus!

When he got to Jesus,
Barty threw himself at Jesus' feet
and said:
"Thank you, thank you,
thank you, Jesus!
I was a leper
— despised and feared by everyone —
and now
you have made me better.
Thank you!"

Jesus pulled Barty to his feet.
He smiled broadly at Barty
because he was happy too.

To the one leper
who had come back
to say thank you
Jesus said:
"Off you go, Barty.
You have shown that you believe.
You have been saved."

With that
Barty let out one last "yippee!",
and off he went,
running, hopping, skipping
and praising God.

And Jesus and his friends
went on with their journey.

Jesus had helped ten people,
and only one had said
thank you.

Do we remember to say
"thank you" to Jesus?

"But Barty", Jesus said,
"I remember ten lepers.
Where are the others?
You are the only one
who has come back to thank me
— and you're not even a local lad."

Do you remember
what the other nine were doing . . .

They were dancing
and singing, eating
and drinking at their party.

They had forgotten Jesus.

Note for parents:
This story can be found in the Gospel of Luke, chapter 17, verses 11-19.

Becky Gets Better

The Good News from Jesus gives life and health to everyone. Jesus likes to be asked into our lives to raise us up — just as Becky was.

Becky was a happy little girl.

She had lots of friends
and they used to come round to play
each day after school.

Her mummy and daddy loved her
very much,

and so did the servants
who looked after the house.

One day
Becky was playing with her friends
when she suddenly felt ill.

Her head started thumping
and her legs felt like jelly.

"Sorry," she said to her friends,
"I'll have to go inside.
See you tomorrow if I'm better."

But the trouble was
Becky did not get better.

She felt more and more ill
  and nothing the doctors gave her
  made her feel better at all.

In fact, she was so ill that her parents
  thought she was dying.

One day,
  as he sat by her bedside,
  her father, Jairus, thought to himself:
  'I wonder if that prophet
  I've heard about could help Becky.
  They say he makes people better.
  Now, what's his name?
  Ah, yes, Jesus is what they call him.
  It's worth a try.'

So Jairus set out to find Jesus.

As usual,
  Jesus was out talking to people,
  dropping a kind word to an old lady,
  telling off a young man for being naughty,
  and curing and comforting
  people who were ill.

Jairus stood near Jesus
  and waited his turn to speak.

Just as Jesus turned to Jairus,
  one of Jairus' servants ran up.

With tears in his eyes he said to Jairus:

"I have come to tell you that Becky has died.
  There is no need to bother Jesus now."

Everybody loved Becky
and they were all very sad
when they heard she had died.

There were men playing sad tunes on
musical instruments,
because that was what they did
in Nazareth at that time.

When Jesus saw the crowd
he said: "Don't cry.
Becky is not dead, she is sleeping."

But Jesus overheard what the man
had said and replied:
"Don't worry; just have faith.

Your daughter will be well again.
Please take me to her."

In spite of the comforting words
Jesus spoke
it was a sad little group
that set off to Jairus' house.

They had seen Jesus make people better,
but Becky was dead:
the journey was a waste of time,
they thought.

Back at the house a big crowd
of friends and relatives had gathered.

Well,
they all knew the difference
between someone
who was sleeping and
someone who was dead!

They all fell about laughing
at Jesus.
What a silly thing to say!

Jesus told the crowd to go home
and allowed only
Becky's parents
and his own special friends
Peter, John and James
to go into the room
where Becky lay.

Jesus took Becky's hand
and said quietly:
"Get up, Becky."

And, would you believe it,
Becky did get up!

She was alive and well
before their very eyes!

When everyone in the room
had finished
hugging each other
and jumping up and down,
Jesus said to them:
"Becky must be starving.
Get her some food."

And he made them all
promise solemnly that
they would not say
a word to anyone.

As for Becky — well,
she was all ready
to play again.

She collected all her friends together
and they all played
as if nothing had happened.

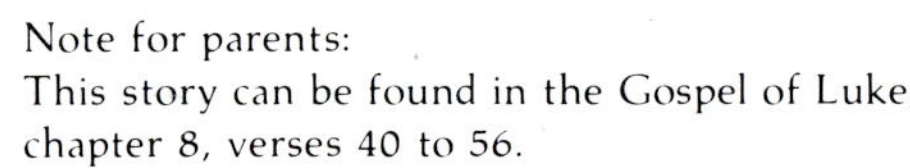

Note for parents:
This story can be found in the Gospel of Luke, chapter 8, verses 40 to 56.

But Becky and Jesus knew
that something had happened.